THE DAFY

AN A–TO–Z OF ORDINARY WORDS
WITH QUITE EXTRAORDINARY
MEANINGS!

HUNDREDS OF UNIQUE
DAFFYNITIONS!!

NO OTHER DICTIONARY LIKE IT
IN THE WORLD!!!

GUARANTEED USELESS
AT SCHOOL!!!!

WON'T TEACH YOU A THING!!!!!!

DESTINED TO BECOME A
WORLD-WIDE BEST-SELLER!!!!!!!

A CLASSIC IN ANY
LANGUAGE!!!!!!!!!*

*Except perhaps English

Other books by GYLES BRANDRETH

DOMINO GAMES AND PUZZLES
NUMBER GAMES AND PUZZLES
GAMES AND PUZZLES WITH COINS AND MATCHES
PENCIL AND PAPER GAMES AND PUZZLES
HOTCHPOTCH
THE ROYAL QUIZ BOOK
BRAIN-TEASERS AND MIND-BENDERS
PROJECT: CASTLES AND HISTORIC HOUSES
EDWARD LEAR'S BOOK OF MAZES
THE BIG BOOK OF SECRETS
THE PUZZLE PARTY FUN BOOK

All published by CORGI-CAROUSEL BOOKS LTD.

THE DAFT DICTIONARY
A CORGI–CAROUSEL BOOK 0 552 54128 1

First published in Great Britain 1978

PRINTING HISTORY
Corgi–Carousel edition published 1978

Corgi–Carousel Books are published by
Transworld Publishers Ltd.
Century House,
61–63 Uxbridge Road,
Ealing, London W.5

Printed in Great Britain by
Fletcher & Son Ltd, Norwich

THE DAFT DICTIONARY

GYLES BRANDRETH

Illustrated by Ian West

CORGI CAROUSEL

A Division of Transworld Publishers Ltd.

HOW TO USE THIS DICTIONARY

If you find you have a table or chair around the house that is a bit wobbly, place the dictionary under the table or chair leg that is causing the wobble.

ACORN

an oak in a nutshell

AUTOGRAPH

a chart showing the sales figures of cars

ATTACK

a small nail

AUCTIONEER

a man who looks
forbidding

ASHTRAY

a place where people
put out their cigar-
ettes when the room
doesn't have a carpet

ARREST

something you take
when you're tired

APRICOTS

beds for baby
monkeys

APPEAR

something you fish off

ANNOUNCE

one-sixteenth of a pound

ACTOR

a man who tries to be everything but himself

ADULT

a person who has stopped growing at both ends and started growing in the middle

ADVERTISING

makes you think you've longed all your life for something when you've never even heard of it

ATOM

a male pussy cat

ABYSS

an Abbot's wife

AUTOBIOGRAPHY

a car's log book

APEX

a female gorilla

ANTELOPE

when two insects run off to get married without their parents knowing

ANTI-FREEZE

a female relative from Iceland

ANTIBODY

uncle's fat wife

ASTRONOMER

a night watchman

ARCHEOLOGIST

a man whose career
lies in ruins

ATOMIC BOMB

something that makes
molehills out of
mountains

ALARM CLOCK

something to scare
the daylight **into** you

ABUNDANCE

222 dancing cakes

ARMIES

the things you've got
up your sleevies

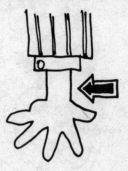

AREA CODE

a cold that hits one
part of the country at
a time

AFFORD

a car some people
drive

BACTERIA

the rear of a cafeteria

BEETROOT

a potato with very high blood pressure

BEE

a hum-bug

BATHING BEAUTY

a girl worth wading
for

BARBER'S SHOP

a clip joint

BOYCOTT

a small bed that's no
good for girls

BUTTRESS

a dairy maid who
makes butter

BULLETIN

a can of corned beef

BALLYHOO

a directory of well-known ballet dancers correctly called *The Ballyhoo's Hoo*

BLUBBER

weeping and whaling

BLAZER

a fire that looks like a jacket

BELLICOSE

a warm, fat stomach

BASHFUL

a retired boxer

BAREFACED

looking like a bear

BARBARIAN

the man who cuts
your hair badly

BLUNDERBUSS

a vehicle that goes
from Edinburgh to
Glasgow taking a
short cut via London

BRUSSELS SPROUT

an ornamental foun-
tain in the Belgian
capital

BOXER

a fellow who stands
up for the other
fellow's rights

BORE

someone who wants
to tell you about
himself when you
want to tell him
about yourself

BIGAMIST

someone who makes
the same mistake
twice

BUNIONS

what you get when
you cross a rabbit
with a leek

BULLDOZER

a sleeping bull

CANNIBAL

someone who is fed
up with people

CHAIR

headquarters for
hindquarters

CARTOON

a song you sing in the
car

CATERPILLAR

an upholstered worm

COMMENTATOR

a talking spud

CONCEIT

I-strain

CROWBAR

a drinking place for crows

CAMELOT

a herd of dromedaries

CARBUNCLE

an automobile with a dent in it

COINCIDE

the sensible thing to do when it's raining

CABBAGE

the age of a taxi

CONFERENCE

a meeting of the
bored

CACTUS

an overgrown pin
cushion

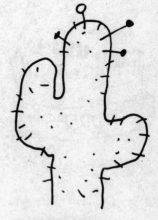

CARNATION

a country where
everyone owns a car

CHARCOAL

what the cleaning
lady puts into the fire

CATACOMB

what goes with the
cat's brush

CARAMEL

a motorised camel

CATASTROPHE

the prize awarded to
the top pussy at the
cat show

COWARD

a man who thinks
with his legs

CLIMATE

the only thing you
can do with a ladder

CAULIFLOWER

the blossom a dog
wears in his button
hole

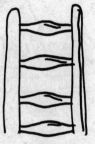

COMMITTEE

a body that keeps
minutes and wastes
hours

CRIMINAL

one who gets caught

CHAMPAGNE

the French for 'false window'

CROSSROADS

angry motorways

CLOAK

the sound made by a Chinese frog

CAMEL

a warped horse

COCOON

a wound-up
caterpillar

CHIPMUNK

a French friar

CELLMATES

two germs living
together

CARPET

material bought by
the yard and worn
out by the foot

CRANE

a bird trained to lift
extremely heavy
weights

DENIAL

where Cleopatra
lived

DENTIST

someone who always
looks down in the
mouth

DRILL SERGEANT

an army dentist

DEPTH

height turned upside down

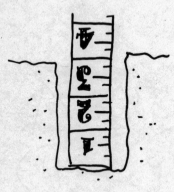

DULCET

a boring tennis match

DIATRIBE

an extinct race

DOLDRUMS

percussion instruments played by girls

28

DRAWING ROOM

where a dentist works

DIAGRAM

a record player that's broken

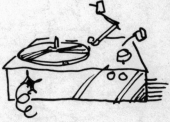

DURATION

an oration that never stops

DISCONSOLATE

a record being played after midnight

DACHSHUND

half a dog high by a
dog and a half long

DIPLOMAT

one who thinks twice
before saying nothing

EXPERIENCE

what people call their
mistakes

EPITAPH

a statement that lies
above about the per-
son that lies below

ECHO

the only thing that
can't stop you getting
the last word

ELECTRICIAN

a switch doctor

EARWIG

a piece of false hair
worn over the ears

EROS

brave people

EQUINOX

strange tapping
noises usually heard
in haunted houses
after dark

EXPERT

someone who used to
be a Pert

ENGLISH CHANNEL

a British television
station

ERASER

what the artist's wife
said when she saw
him drawing a nude

EXTINCT

a dead skunk

EVE

what you shout at the
start of a tug-o'-war

ELLIPTICAL

a kiss from a man
with a moustache

FLOOD

a river that's too big
for its bridges

FRUSTRATE

in the top class

FORTUNE

a singing quartet

FARTHINGALE

a cheap hurricane

FACTORY

a set of encyclopaedias

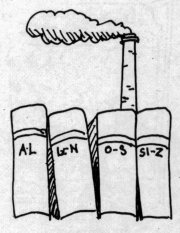

FASTIDIOUS

someone who is quick
and ugly

FUGUE

a thick fog

FAUCET

what you have to do
when the door is
jammed

FIDDLESTICK

something you use to
play the violin

FLEECE

insects that get into your
wool if you don't
wash regularly

FIGMENT

what Adam and Eve
wore in the Garden
of Eden

FLATTERY

a battery that's run
out of power

FRIEND

someone who has the
same enemies as you

FJORD

a Norwegian motor
car

FORUM

Two-um plus two-um

GALLOWS

where no noose is
good noose

GOSSIP

letting the chat out of
the bag

GOBLET

a small turkey

GANGRENE

a group of Martians

GALLERY

a home for girls

GRANARY

a home for grannies

GONDOLIER

when you've wiped
the grin off your face

GENERALLY

an Arab general

HUMBUG

a musical insect

HAIR TONIC

medicine for rabbits

HATCHET

what a hen does to an egg

HYACINTH

what you say when
you first meet Lady
Cynthia

HERMIT

a lady's glove

HAY

high-class grass

HOGWASH

a pig's laundry

HACKNEYED

the opposite of knock-kneed

HYPOCHONDRIAC

a person with an infinite capacity for faking pains

HATLESS

the strong man who carried the world on his shoulders

HONESTY

fear of getting caught

HOSPITALS

places where people
who are run down
wind up

HUG

a roundabout way of
expressing affection

HYPOCRITE

a man who sets a
good example when
other people are watch-
ing

HIPPIES

the things you hang
your leggies on

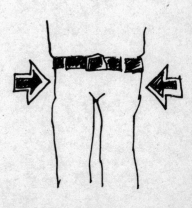

HOLIDAY

the time when you
find out where **not** to
go next year

ILLEGAL

a sick bird of prey

IGLOO

an icicle made for two

ICED LOLLY

Eskimo money

IGNORANCE

when you don't know
something and
somebody finds out

IRONY

the instrument used
for pressing clothes
on an ironing board

IDOLISE

lazy eyeballs

INCOME

you try to make it
first, then you try to
make it last

IMPIOUS

a religious elf

IMPALE

white-faced Red
Indian

INKLING

a very small pen

INTENSE

a camping holiday

ICE

skid stuff

INCONGRUOUS

where American laws
are made

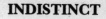

INFORMATION

how planes fly at an
air show

INDISTINCT

where the dirty dishes
go

ICEBERG

a kind of permanent
wave

ICICLE

an eavesdropper

IMPASSABLE

a slippery football

ICE CREAM

but only when I'm
frightened

IMPROVEMENT

a guest who is always
welcome to stay, as in
'There's always room
for improvement'

G.W. IMPROVEMENT

JUMP

the last word in aero-planes

JAYWALKING

a hobby that gives you that run-down feeling

JODHPURS

the noise made by two happy cats

JUGULAR

shaped like a Grecian
urn

JOKE

something not every-
body gets

KIDNEY

the knee of a baby goat

KNOB

a thing to adore

KINDRED

a fear of being visited by relatives

LETTUCE SALAD

correspondence you
can eat

LEOPARD

a dotted lion, as in 'to
open this packet tear
along dotted lion'

LITHE

falsehoods told by
someone who lisps

LATTICE

a green window
much liked by rabbits

LOBSTER

a tennis player

LOGARITHMS

wooden dance tunes

LOST CHORD

something you look for
when playing Haydn
seek (after you've been
to the shops with your
Chopin Liszt)

LAUNDRY

a place where clothes
are mangled

LUXURY

something that costs
£5 to make and £105
to sell

LUCK

when a man picks up
a horse-shoe on the
road, and is knocked
by a car into a field of
four-leaf clovers as a
black cat walks by

LIGHT SLEEPER

someone who goes to
bed in a chandelier

LYRE

a dishonest harp

MINIMUM

Minidad's wife

MITTENS

what you get when a
cat swallows a ball of
wool

MONEY

the Royal Mint
makes it first and you
try to make it last

MONOLOGUE

an unmarried piece
of wood

MALADY

a duchess

MELANCHOLY

a dogs that likes
melons

MUSHROOM

the place where they
cook school dinners

MUMMY

an Egyptian pressed
for time

MOTEL

William Tell's sister

MISTLETOE

astronaut's athlete's
foot

MAGPIE

a pudding made with
old magazines

MARGIN

mummy's favourite tonic

MOUNTEBANK

the place where the Canadian police keep their money

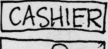

MOSQUITO

a flying hypodermic needle

MOUNTAIN RANGE

a cooker made specially for use at high altitudes

MOUNTAIN CLIMBER

a man who always wants to take one more peak

MACARONI

the inventor of the wireless who used his noodle and pasta message through spaghetti

MINCE

white sweet with a hole in the middle and a peppermint flavour

MERMAID

a creature that's half a girl and half a sardine

METER

a butcher with a car

MACAROON

a famous Scots biscuit

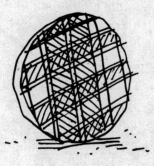

MISFIRED

a secretary who has been given the sack

MUSTARD

the only thing that stays hot in the fridge

FROZEN MUSTARD

MULTIPLICATION TABLE

the longest table in
the world

NUMBER

the first thing to take when you're run down

NUDIST CAMP

a place where hardly anything goes on

NORTH POLE

someone who comes from Warsaw

NECTAR

a garment worn
round the neck

NIGHTINGALE

an evening out in a
storm

NAIL

a long thin pointed
object with a flat
head which you aim
at while hitting your
thumb with a
hammer

NUDIST

someone who goes
around without a
vest, a shirt or a
jacket and wears
trousers to match

MATCHING WARDROBE

OBESITY

surplus gone to waist

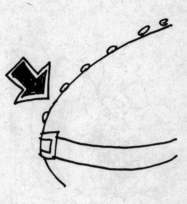

OPPORTUNIST

someone who meets a wolf at the door and the next day appears wearing a fur coat

OPTIMISM

the cheerful spirit that makes it possible for a kettle to whistle with boiling water up its nose

OPERETTA

the person who answers when you dial 100 on the telephone

OUT OF BOUNDS

an exhausted kangaroo

OTTOMAN

a car mechanic

OPTIMIST

a hope addict

OYSTER

what you shout when you want someone to lift up your mother

OCTOPUS

a cat with eight feet

OBOE

a tramp

ODIOUS

poetry that stinks

OBLIQUE

time to call in the plumber

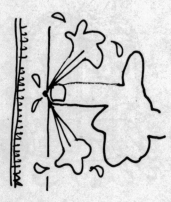

OMELETTE

Prince of Denmark, a play by William Shakespeare rich in fowl play and eggsitement

POLYGON

a dead parrot

PRICKLY PEAR

two hedgehogs

PINE

what sad fir trees do

PANTS

what trousers do on a long run up a steep hill

PACIFIST

someone who punches you on the nose peacefully

PRUNE

a plum that's seen better days

POLYGAMIST

a parrot with more than one wife

PAINFUL

a glass house
(Please remember
that people who live
in glass houses should
undress in the
basement)

PHONOGRAPH

a chart used by the
Post Office to record
telephone sales

PALAVER

a kind of sweater

PHARMACY

the science of
agriculture

PARKING SPACE

always filled with
somebody else's car

PAVEMENT ARTIST

someone who draws
pictures on his knees

PARADOX

two doctors

PSYCHIATRIST

someone who doesn't
have to worry as long
as other people do

PARATROOPER

an Army drop-out

PHYSICIST

a man who makes
ginger beer

PEA

a vegeta-pill

POULTRY

a tree that chickens
like roosting in

PUTTY

miniature golf

PIGEON-TOED

half-pigeon, half-toad

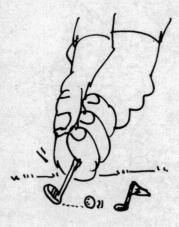

PROPAGANDA

a well-behaved and
upper-class goose

PRINTER

a man of letters

POSSE

a cat from the Wild West

POPULACE

frilly material that people like

PROFESSOR

a textbook wired for sound

POLITICS

a parrot that's swallowed a watch

PASTEURISE

too far to see

PYRAMID

an organised pile of
Egyptian rocks

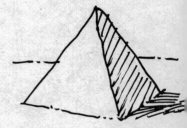

PARACHUTE

a double-barrelled
shotgun

PARTY

Dad's supper

PUPILS

what a cross-eyed
teacher can't control

PEN FRIENDS

pigs that get on well
together

PORCUPINE

an unhappy slice of
bacon

PYGMY

a tiny pig (Shakespeare
wrote about one in his
play *Hamlet*)

PRAWN

one of the small
pieces used in the
game of Chess

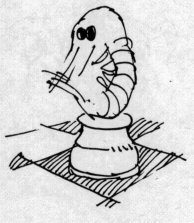

PILLOW

headquarters

PICKLE

a cucumber in a spot
of bother

PORTABLE

a cheap piece of
furniture to eat off

PANTRY

the room where you
keep your underwear

PIPECLEANER

a toothpick wearing
long woolly under-
wear

Q

a long line that people stand in

QUACK

a duck's doctor

QUAKER

a nervous lady

QUICKSAND

the reason the hour-glass is ten minutes' fast

QUADRUPLETS

four crying out loud!

QUINCE

five children at one time

QUATRAIN

a railway train with four carriages

RUBBER BAND

see

STRING QUARTET

RUNNER BEANS

special food for
athletes

RINGLEADER

the first one in the
bath

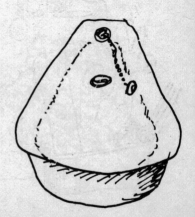

RAZOR

an alarm clock for
girls

RECITED

going back to take a
second look

RESEARCH

looking for something
twice

RUBBER GLOVES

things you put on
when you want to
wash your hands
without getting them
wet

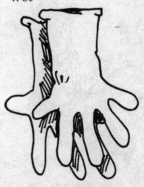

RAISIN

a very old and very
anxious grape

RECLUSE

a Chinaman going on
his second cruise

REBATE

putting another
worm onto the hook

ROMANCE

ants in Rome

RAWHIDE

a nudist's clothes

RUGGED

feeling tough when you're sitting on the carpet

REORIENTATE

a Chinaman returning to China

RANSOM

a four-minute miler

RHUBARB

bloodshot celery

RAGAMUFFIN

a toasted teacake
made from old
clothes

ROTUNDA

an author's pen
name, as in 'Samuel
Clemens rotunda the
name Mark Twain'

REPARTEE

the second party
you've been to this
week

SAGO

how you start a
pudding race

SIGNATURE

a baby swan's
autograph

STRING QUARTET

see
RUBBER BAND

SEE-SAW

what you use to cut
through giant waves

SEA SHELLS

what you fire from
underwater guns

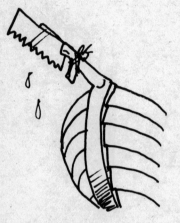

SINGING

your bathright

SECRET

something you tell
everybody one by
one

SANDWICH

an attempt to make
both ends meat

SCULPTOR

someone who makes
faces

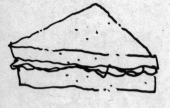

SELF-CONTROL

someone who can
open a bag of peanuts
and eat just one

SYNONYM

a word you use in
place of one you can't
spell

SNOW

well-dressed rain

SAGE

a man who knows his onions

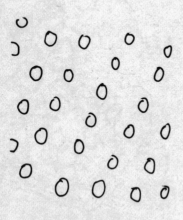

SPELLBOUND

the way a dictionary is covered

STABILISED

a horse that's locked in and can't get out

SONATA

Mr. and Mrs. Ata's
eldest boy

SCRAPBOOK

a boxer's diary

SHAMROCK

a phoney rock

SHAMPOO

a phoney smell

SNUFF

no more, as in 'That's snuff, thank you, I'm full up'

SOMERSAULT

what goes with pepper from May to September

SHOTGUN

an exhausted gun

SLEEPING BAG

a nap sack

SQUARE ROOT

a diced turnip

SNORING

sheet music

SUSPICIOUS SOUNDING

an elephant hanging over the edge of a cliff with its tail tied to a daisy

SKELETON

a guy inside out with his outside off

SICK REPTILE

an illigator

SCALES

the part of a fish that
weighs the most

SPRINGTIME

the moment you sit
on a drawing pin

SKINDIVER

a mosquito

TOMORROW

today's greatest
labour-saving
device

TRICYCLE

a tot rod

TEARS

glum drops

TROJAN HORSE

a phoney pony

TRANSPARENT

Dad or Mum in a trance

TAXIDERMIST

a stuffed cab driver

TEMPEST

an ill-tempered little nuisance

TYRANT

someone who gets
into a temper when he
can't tie his tie
properly

TELEVISION

radio with eyestrain

TONGUE TWISTER

something that gets
your tang tongueled

TUBE

in English it means a
hollow cylinder, but
in Dutch it means a
silly Hollander

UNABRIDGED

a river you have to
swim across

UNDERCOVER
AGENT

a spy in bed

ULTRAMARINE

the best sailor in the
entire navy

UNISON

an only boy

UNIT

a term of abuse, as in 'Can't you even spell apple correctly, unit!'

VITAMIN

what you do when
someone comes
round to see you

VESTRY

the room where you
keep your vests

VOLCANO

a mountain that's
blown its stack

VOWEL

cheating in sport, as
in 'he's definitely
guilty of vowel play'

WATCHDOG

an animal that goes 'Woof, tick, woof, tick, woof, tick'

WAITER

someone who thinks money grows on trays

WEDDING RING

a metal tourniquet worn on the left hand to stop circulation

WHOLESOME

the only thing in the world you can take whole and still have some left

WALKIE-TALKIE

a parrot out for a stroll

WASHABLE

giving a bath to a bull

WATER

thirst-aid

WIND

air in a hurry

WINTER

twelve months in England

WINDOW SHOPPING

going out to buy new windows for the house

WHISKY

two pints of which make one cavort

WINE

the noise made by an
unhappy bottle of
alcohol

WOODWORM

a do-it-yourself
carpenter

WIRELESS

a human puppet

WOE

the opposite of
'giddy-up'

X-RAY

bellyvision

XYLOPHONE

revolutionary
instrument invented
in 1860 by Alexander
Graham Xylo

X

what hens lay

YELLOW

what you do when
you stub your toe

YESMEN

the people who are
around the fellow
nobody noes

YEAR

are you listening, as
in 'D'year what I
said just now?'

ZEBRA

a horse that's escaped from prison

ZINC

the place you wash the zaucepans

ZUB

noise made by a bee flying backwards

There are 72 letters in the Cambodian alphabet. Consider yourself lucky that you got given the English edition of the Daft Dictionary.